THE OFFICIAL PETERBOROUGH UNITED QUIZ BOOK

THE OFFICIAL PETERBOROUGH UNITED QUIZ BOOK

Compiled by Chris Cowlin
and Kevin Snelgrove

Foreword by Barry Fry

APEX PUBLISHING LTD

Hardback first published in 2008 by
Apex Publishing Ltd
PO Box 7086, Clacton on Sea, Essex, CO15 5WN, England
www.apexpublishing.co.uk

British Library Cataloguing-in-Publication Data
A catalogue record for this book
is available from the British Library

ISBN HARDBACK: 1-906358-46-X   978-1-906358-46-4

Typeset in 10.5pt Chianti Bdlt Win95BT

Cover Design: Siobhan Smith

Printed and bound in Great Britain by
Biddles Ltd., King's Lynn, Norfolk

Author's Note:
Please can you contact me: **ChrisCowlin@btconnect.com** if you find any mistakes/errors in this book as I would like to put them right on any future reprints of this book. I would also like to hear from Peterborough United fans who have enjoyed the test! For more information on me and my books please look at: **www.ChrisCowlin.com**

This book is an official product of Peterborough United Football Club.

We would like to dedicate this book to:

All the players and staff who have worked for the club during their history.

FOREWORD

First of all, can I say that it is a privilege to be asked to provide the foreword for this official Peterborough United quiz book. I joined the football club in August 1996 as owner/manager. Some 12 years later I can reflect on many ups and downs. I would like to thank the many people whom have helped me enormously in keeping the club in existence. It has been a long hard battle but all the pain has been worth it with the arrival of our new messiah Darragh MacAnthony.

Since the chairman first walked in to London Road he has become a breath of fresh air with his enthusiasm, love, passion and knowledge for the wonderful game which we call football not to mention his financial expertise. He has completely transformed the club and has become like the pied piper with many wanting to follow him along to the Promised Land. He has not only changed the outlook of the club but also the whole City has sat up and took notice of his ambitions, and wants to be a part of the progress.

Darragh also had the guts to put his money where his mouth was in securing the transfers of Aaron Mclean, Craig Mackail - Smith, George Boyd, Shane Blackett, Craig Morgan, and Micah Hyde before appointing another young ambitious man to be his manager – Darren Ferguson. Darren has since had the total backing of the chairman in securing more young hungry players like Joe Lewis, Russell Martin, Chris Westwood, Charlie Lee, Scott Rendell, Dean Keates, Paul Coutts Chris Whelpdale, Tommy Williams, Sergio Torres, Shaun Batt, and Dominic Green. So as you can see our chairman's commitment to bring success to The Posh has been second to none.

In their first year together both Darragh and Darren had a goal which was to gain promotion which they did by playing the best football seen at London Road in the last 50 years. Playing fast, exciting, entertaining, skilful football and scoring more than 100 goals in all competitions.

Since the arrival of Darragh MacAnthony (not to mention his financial expertise) The Posh are a force to be reckoned with. With the ambition of the chairman to gain another promotion to the championship and move into a new all seater stadium followed by promotion to the Premiership it is a great time to be a Peterborough Untied supporter.

I hope you enjoy the book and I would like to thank you for your support it is very much appreciated by everybody at Peterborough United Football Club.

Up The Posh!

Best wishes
Barry Fry

INTRODUCTION

I would first of all like to thank Barry Fry for writing the foreword to this book. He is a true legend for The Posh and I doubt I have ever seen anyone more passionate for winning football matches. I am very grateful for his help on this project.

I would also like to thank all the past legends of Peterborough United Football Club and many current employees of the club for their comments and reviews on this book (these can be found at the back of the book).

I would also like to thank Amber Fry for her help and advice during the books compilation.

I hope you enjoy this book. Hopefully it should bring back some wonderful memories!

It was great working with Kevin Snelgrove again, who is very well organised, between us I hope we have given you a selection of easy, medium and hard questions.

In closing, I would like to thank all my friends and family for encouraging me to complete this book.

Chris Cowlin.

Best wishes
Chris Cowlin

Visit Chris Cowlin's website:

www.ChrisCowlin.com

Visit Kevin Snelgrove's website:

www.KevinSnelgrove.co.uk

HISTORY OF THE CLUB

1. In what year was Peterborough United football club founded?

2. What is Peterborough United's nickname?

3. What is the name of Peterborough United's ground?

4. What was the original name of Peterborough United before it ceased to exist in 1932?

5. In what year was Peterborough United elected into Division Four of the Football League?

6. Following on from the previous question, which team did Peterborough United replace in the Football League?

7. Can you name Peterborough United's two longest serving managers?

8. Which two clubs are considered Peterborough's local rivals?

9. Which player scored 52 League goals for Peterborough United in their first season in the Football League?

10. On 21 January 2007 Darren Ferguson took over as manager of Peterborough United. Can you name his famous father?

WHO AM I? – 1

11.　*I was born in 1984 and am a centre forward. I signed from Dagenham & Redbridge in January 2007. I scored a hat-trick against Bristol Rovers in a 5-4 home League win during September 2008.*

12.　*I signed from Norwich City in 2008 and play in goal. I also spent time on loan to Stockport and Morecambe during 2007.*

13.　*I scored 20 League, 1 League Cup and 3 FA Cup goals during 1997/1998 for the club, finishing their highest scorer for the season.*

14.　*I signed for the club in May 2007 from Walsall. I am a defender and played for Hartlepool United between 1999 and 2005.*

15.　*I scored for the club on my second appearance, whilst on loan from Fulham in 2008. I scored the equaliser in a 2-2 home draw against Tranmere Rovers during September 2008.*

16.　*I hold the record for being the club's highest League scorer in a season, with 52 goals during 1960/1961.*

17.　*I managed the club during the 1977/1978 season.*

18.　*I was the club's highest League scorer with 10 goals during 1988/1989, finishing 3 goals ahead of David Longhurst.*

19.　*I am a goalkeeper and won the club's Player of the Year award during 1992/1993.*

20.　*I was the only Peterborough player to play in every League match during 1986/1987 and also scored the winning goal against Hereford United in a 2-1 home win during March 1987.*

CLUB RECORDS

21. Which player scored 122 League goals for Peterborough United between 1967 and 1975?

22. A record attendance of 30,096 saw Peterborough United draw 0-0 in the FA Cup 5th round on 20 February 1965, against which team?

23. How many League goals did Peterborough United score in the Division Four season of 1960/1961?

24. Peterborough United's record FA Cup victory was on 6 October 1945 away to Rushden Town. What was the result?

25. Following on from the previous question, which player scored six goals in the game, achieving a club record?

26. How many League appearances did Tommy Robson make for Peterborough between 1968 and 1981?

27. For which player did Peterborough United receive a record transfer fee of £700,000 from Tottenham Hotspur in December 1999?

28. In July 1996 Peterborough United paid £350,000 to which club for the services of Martyn O'Connor?

29. Which Peterborough goalkeeper kept seven consecutive clean sheets between 6 October and 10 November 1973?

30. Whom did Peterborough United beat 9-1 to record their record League victory on 5 September 1998?

THE LEAGUE CUP

31. Which Hampshire-based team did the club beat 2-1 at home in the 1st round during August 2007?

32. Which East Anglian team did the club beat 4-2 on penalties after a 2-2 draw in the 1st round during August 2006?

33. Following on from the previous question, can you name the two Peterborough scorers in the match?

34. Who scored the goal when Peterborough beat Fulham 1-0 away in the 3rd round during October 1975?

35. Which London team did Peterborough beat 4-1 on aggregate over the two legs in the 1st round during August and September 1990?

36. Which team knocked the club out of the competition by beating them 1-0 in the 4th round, after a replay and extra time, with Bjørn Kristensen scoring for the winning side?

37. Who scored a brace for Peterborough in the 4-2 home win in the 1st round, 2nd leg, during September 1982?

38. Which midfielder scored for Peterborough in the 2-1 away defeat to Bristol City in the 1st round in August 2008?

39. Which Welsh team did the club beat 3-0 at home in the 1st round, 2nd leg, during August 1995?

40. Following on from the previous question, which midfielder scored a brace in the game?

CLUB HONOURS

Match the honour with the year in which it was achieved by Peterborough

41.	Division Four Champions (first time)	1992
42.	League Cup semi-finalists	2000
43.	Finished 10th in Division One	1974
44.	Promoted to Division Two via play-offs (second time)	1961
45.	Division Four champions (second time)	1956
46.	Promoted to Division Three	2008
47.	Promoted to Division Two via play-offs (first time)	1966
48.	League Two runners-up	1993
49.	Reached the 6th round of the FA Cup	1991
50.	Midland League champions (first time)	1965

SIMON DAVIES

51. In what year was Simon born – 1977, 1978 or 1979?

52. How many League goals did Simon score during his Peterborough career?

53. What nationality is Simon?

54. How many League appearances did Simon make during 1999/2000?

55. Following on from the previous question, which fellow Peterborough player signed for the same club at the same time?

56. Which London club did Simon sign for in January 2007 from Everton?

57. Against which team did Simon make his debut for Peterborough in a 3-1 away defeat in January 1998, having come on as a substitute?

58. How many League goals did Simon score for Peterborough during 1998/1999?

59. Against which Essex-based team did Simon score the only goal in a 1-0 away win during September 1999?

60. Can you name the two other scorers when Simon scored against Chester City in a 3-0 home win during September 1998?

WHERE DID THEY GO? – 1

*Match the player with the club he moved
to on leaving Peterborough United*

61.	George Berry	Norwich City
62.	Jimmy Bullard	Carlisle United
63.	Adam Newton	Hartlepool United
64.	David Seaman	Wigan Athletic
65.	David Rogers	Preston North End
66.	George Swindin	Chester City
67.	Adam Drury	Birmingham City
68.	Matthew Etherington	Brentford
69.	Simon Yeo	Tottenham Hotspur
70.	Alan Waddle	Arsenal

2008/2009

71. Who was the manager of Peterborough during this season?

72. Against which London club did the club record their first League win, in a 2nd round match during August 2008?

73. Which team did Peterborough beat 5-4 at London Road on 6 September 2008?

74. Following on from the previous question, which Peterborough striker scored a hat-trick in the game?

75. Which squad number was given to Tom Williams during this season?

76. Which team did The Posh beat 2-1 away on 27 September 2008?

77. Following on from the previous question, which Midfielder scored the winning goal for The Posh?

78. The Posh beat Leeds United 2-0 at London Road on 4 October 2008, whcih two players scored the goals?

79. Which squad number was given to Scott Rendell during this season?

80. Which team were 2-0 up at London Road after 30 minutes, only for Peterborough to score twice and clinch a 2-2 draw during September 2008?

MANACERS – 1

Match the manager with the period he was in charge at Peterborough United

81.	Peter Morris	1989-90
82.	Jack Fairbrother	2006-07
83.	John Wile	1950-52
84.	John Still	1979-82
85.	Keith Alexander	1972-77
86.	Jock Porter	1994-95
87.	Noel Cantwell	1967-69
88.	Mark Lawrenson	1983-86
89.	Norman Rigby	1934-36
90.	Bob Gurney	1962-64

2007/2008

91.   Who was Peterborough's manager during this season?

92.   Which team did Peterborough beat 7-0 at home in the League during November 2007?

93.   Following on from the previous question, who scored a hat-trick in the game?

94.   Can you name the two players that each scored a brace in the 4-0 home League win against Lincoln during March 2008?

95.   Can you name the team that that club beat 3-0 at home on the opening day of the League season during August 2007?

96.   In what position in the League did the club finish – 2nd, 3rd or 4th?

97.   Who was the club's highest League scorer with 29 goals in 45 appearances?

98.   Following on from the previous question, can you name the other two players who finished on double figures, both scoring 12 League goals?

99.   Who scored the only goal in the 1-0 home win against Chester City during March 2008?

100.   Who scored an 88th minute winner in a 2-1 home win against Bradford City during December 2007?

NATIONALITIES – 1

Match the player with his nationality

101.	Sergio Torres	English
102.	Aidy Boothroyd	Irish Republican
103.	Tom Williams	Argentinean
104.	Micah Hyde	English
105.	Jimmy Rooney	Welsh
106.	Ken Charlery	Jamaican
107.	Craig Morgan	Australian
108.	Gary Breen	English-Cypriot
109.	Jimmy Bullard	Irish Republican
110.	Dick Whittaker	St Lucian

WHO AM I? – 2

111. I was the first player to see League action in two separate spells with The Posh in 1964-66 and 1966-68.

112. I am a Welsh centre-back who was captain of The Posh in the mid-sixties.

113. I joined Peterborough United at the age of 31 from Bournemouth for £25,000 in August 1988.

114. I was in the Hearts team which won the Scottish Cup in 1956 and moved to Peterborough in 1964 and went onto make 172 League appearances.

115. I am a goalkeeper and joined The Posh in December 1973 on loan from Newcastle United and stayed until 1977 when I left to join Brighton & Hove Albion for £18,000.

116. I was the club's leading League scorer during the 1987/1988 season, with 18 goals in 44 appearances.

117. I started and played in all 46 League games during 1990/1991. I also won Player of the Year during the season.

118. I am a midfielder who signed for the club on New Year's Day 2007. During the 2008/2009 season I wore the number 10 shirt.

119. I am a midfielder and signed for the club in January 2007 from Burnley. I also played for Watford between 1998 and 2004.

120. I managed the club between December 1992 and December 1993. Further in my career I managed Luton Town for a short period, between November 2000 and February 2001.

WHERE DID THEY COME FROM? – 1

Match the player with the team he left to join Peterborough United

121.	George Boyd	Grimsby Town
122.	Derek Dougan	Mansfield Town
123.	Clive Platt	Walsall
124.	Chris Westwood	Stevenage Borough
125.	Tim Ryan	Charlton Athletic
126.	Danny Crow	Notts County
127.	Bradley Allen	Barnet
128.	Liam Hatch	Doncaster Rovers
129.	Willie Duff	Aston Villa
130.	Aidy Boothroyd	Norwich City

DEBUTS

*Match up the fixture with the player who made
his debut in the match*

131. v. Rochdale (home),
      August 2007, 3-0 League win   Martin O'Connor

132. v. Southend United (away),
      August 2008, 1-0 League defeat   John McGlashan

133. v. Bristol Rovers (away),
      August 1996, 1-0 League defeat   Grant Haley

134. v. Southend United (home),
      October 1999, 1-0 League win   Ricky Heppolette

135. v. Tranmere Rovers (home),
      August 1984, 1-0 League win   Dean Keates

136. v. Lincoln City (away),
      August 1979, 1-0 League win   Roger Willis

137. v. Bristol Rovers (away),
      August 1996, 1-0 League defeat   Shane Blackett

138. v. Southend United (home),
      January 1993, 1-0 League win   David Johnson

139. v. Bristol Rovers (away),
      February 2007, 3-2 League defeat   Scott Houghton

140. v. Bristol Rovers (away),
      August 1996, 1-0 League defeat   Sergio Torres

POSITIONS IN LEAGUE TWO

*Match the season/points with the position in which
Peterborough United finished in the League*

141.	1994/1995, 60 points	21st
142.	2007/2008, 92 points	9th
143.	2003/2004, 52 points	12th
144.	1995/1996, 52 points	15th
145.	2000/2001, 59 points	11th
146.	2006/2007, 65 points	18th
147.	2001/2002, 55 points	2nd
148.	1996/1997, 47 points	19th
149.	2002/2003, 58 points	17th
150.	2005/2006, 62 points	10th

BARRY FRY

151.   What is Barry's middle name?

152.   In what position did Barry play during his playing days?

153.   Which Essex-based team did Barry manage in 1993?

154.   In what year was Barry appointed Peterborough manager?

155.   Which manager did Barry take over from as the club's manager?

156.   Which team were Barry's opponents in his first League match as manager, a 1-0 away defeat?

157.   True or false: Peterborough were relegated in Barry's first season in charge at the club?

158.   To what position in the League did Barry guide Peterborough during 1999/2000, leading to the club's promotion – 3rd, 4th or 5th?

159.   In what year did Barry step down as manager, becoming the club's Director of Football?

160.   At which top-flight club did Barry start his playing career as an apprentice?

POSITIONS IN LEAGUE THREE

Match the season/points with the position in which Peterborough United finished in the League

161.	1999/2000, 78 points	15th
162.	1962/1963, 51 points	4th
163.	1976/1977, 41 points	10th
164.	1997/1998, 67 points	5th
165.	1964/1965, 51 points	21st
166.	1966/1967, 43 points	16th
167.	1974/1975, 50 points	8th
168.	1998/1999, 66 points	6th
169.	1977/1978, 56 points	9th
170.	1978/1979, 36 points	7th

2006/2007

171. Which team did Peterborough beat 4-1 at home on the opening day of the season?

172. How many League goals did The Posh score in their 46 matches - 70, 80 or 90?

173. In what position did the club finish in the League?

174. How many of the 46 League matches did Peterborough win – 18, 22 or 26?

175. Who finished as the club's highest League scorer, with 8 goals in 13 starts and 2 substitute appearances?

176. Which team did the club beat 5-2 at home during November 2006?

177. Who scored a brace for the club on the last day of the season, in a 3-3 home draw against Rochdale?

178. Can you name the four goalscorers in the 4-0 home win against MK Dons during March 2007?

179. True or false: Peterborough were unbeaten in August 2006 in their first 5 League games?

180. Against which team did the club record their first win in 2007, a 3-0 home win?

SQUAD NUMBERS 2008/2009 – 1

Match the player with his squad number for the season

181.	Craig Morgan	25
182.	James McKeown	3
183.	Charlie Lee	4
184.	Jamie Day	34
185.	Dominic Green	1
186.	Micah Hyde	21
187.	Joe Lewis	6
188.	Tom Williams	17
189.	Mark Tyler	13
190.	Shane Blackett	8

GOALKEEPERS

191.   Who was the club's no. 1 during the 2008/2009
        season?

192.   Which goalkeeper made his debut for the club in a 4-0
        away defeat to Birmingham during September 1994?

193.   Who played in all 46 League games during the
        1974/1975 season?

194.   Against which team did James McKeown make his
        debut for the club, coming on as a substitute during
        February 2008?

195.   Which manager gave David Seaman his debut for
        Peterborough in August 1982?

196.   Can you name the two goalkeepers that played in the
        46 League games during 1990/1991?

197.   Who played in all 46 League games during the
        1992/1993 season?

198.   John Barnwell handed which goalkeeper his debut in
        September 1977, in a 1-0 away win against Sheffield
        Wednesday?

199.   Can you name 3 of the 4 goalkeepers that played in
        Peterborough's 46 League games during 1986/1987?

200.   Who played in all 46 League games during the
        1979/1980 season?

WHERE DID THEY GO? – 2

Match the player with the club he moved to on leaving Peterborough United

201.	Bryn Gunn	Dundee
202.	Pat Gavin	Swindon Town
203.	Ray Hankin	Hull City
204.	Craig Allardyce	Chelmsford City
205.	Martin Carruthers	Northampton Town
206.	Jimmy Quinn	Welling United
207.	Curtis Woodhouse	Colchester United
208.	Lee Power	Darlington
209.	Trevor Whymark	Wolverhampton Wanderers
210.	Gordon Polley	Chesterfield

DARREN FERGUSON

211. In which year was Darren born – 1970, 1971 or 1972?

212. Which top-flight team did Darren play for between 1990 and 1994?

213. In January of what year did Peterborough appoint Darren as manager?

214. In what month during the 2007/2008 season with Peterborough was Darren voted Manager of the Month?

215. Against which Welsh side, a former club of Darren's, did he record his first League win as Peterborough's manager?

216. Which 3 players did Darren sign for The Posh during July 2008?

217. To what position did Darren guide the club in his first season in charge?

218. How many of his 46 League matches in charge did Darren win during 2007/2008 – 28, 29 or 30?

219. For which club did Darren play between 1994 and 1999?

220. In what position did Darren play during his playing days?

MANAGERS – 2

Match the manager with the period he was in charge at Peterborough United

221.	Barry Fry	1988-89
222.	John Barnwell	1954-58
223.	Jimmy Hagan	1938-48
224.	Mark Wright	1977-78
225.	Sam Madden	2006
226.	Jim Iley	1996-2005
227.	Mick Jones	1958-62
228.	Mick Halsall	2005-06
229.	Steve Bleasdale	1969-72
230.	George Swindin	1995-96

JIMMY BULLARD

231. In what position does Jimmy play?

232. In what year did Jimmy sign for The Posh?

233. Following on from the previous question, from which London team did he sign?

234. Which manager handed Jimmy his debut for Peterborough?

235. Against which team did Jimmy score his first Peterborough goal, during September 2001 in a 6-0 home win?

236. How many League goals did Jimmy score during his Peterborough career?

237. For which team did Jimmy sign in January 2003 when he left London Road?

238. Jimmy's last goal for Peterborough was against Swindon Town in the League during November 2002, but what was the final score?

239. Jimmy scored a penalty in a 2-0 home League win against Northampton during October 2001, but who scored the other goal?

240. How many League goals did Jimmy score for Peterborough during 2001/2002?

WHERE DID THEY COME FROM? – 2

Match the player with the team he left to join Peterborough United

241.	Danny Blanchett	Coventry City
242.	Miguel de Souza	Chesterfield
243.	Gary Breen	Tottenham Hotspur
244.	Jim Baron	Wycombe Wanderers
245.	Ernie Moss	Norwich City
246.	Simon Rea	Cambridge City
247.	Trevor Benjamin	Connecticut Bicentennials
248.	Ron Barnes	Birmingham City
249.	Paul Bradshaw	Gillingham
250.	Charlie Lee	West Bromwich Albion

1990s

251. In what year during the 1990s did John Still take over as manager of Peterborough?

252. Who was the club's highest League scorer with 16 goals during 1992/1993?

253. True or false: The Posh were relegated to Division Two at the end of the 1993/1994 season as they finished bottom of the League with 37 points?

254. In what position did the club finish in Division Four during 1990/1991 to gain automatic promotion?

255. Who scored four goals on his debut (whilst on loan) in the 5-2 home win during February 1999 against Barnet?

256. How many players were used in League games during 1995/1996 – 26, 31 or 36?

257. Who was Peterborough's manager during 1991/1992?

258. Who was the club's Player of the Year during 1993/1994?

259. Which rivals did The Posh beat 4-0 at home in the FA Cup 1st round during November 1994, with Ken Charlery (2), Lee Williams and Liburd Henry scoring the goals?

260. Which top-flight team did Peterborough beat 1-0 at home during December 1991 in the 4th round of the League Cup, with Garry Kimble scoring the only goal after 19 minutes?

FA CUP WINS

Match the season/round with the final result

261. 2007/2008, 3rd round   **Peterborough United 2-1 Arsenal**

262. 1982/1983, 2nd round   **Plymouth Argyle 0-1 Peterborough United**

263. 1969/1970, 3rd round   **Peterborough United 5-2 Doncaster Rovers**

264. 1980/1981, 4th round   **Portsmouth 1-2 Peterborough United**

265. 2003/2004, 2nd round   **Colchester United 1-3 Peterborough United**

266. 1970/1971, 1st round   **Peterborough United 3-2 Grimsby Town**

267. 1964/1965, 4th round   **Rotherham United 0-1 Peterborough United**

268. 1960/1961, 3rd round   **Peterborough United 3-1 Southend United**

269. 1973/1974, 3rd round   **Notts County 0-1 Peterborough United**

270. 1996/1997, 3rd round   **Peterborough United 3-1 Wimbledon**

2005/2006

271. Which striker was the club's highest League scorer with 15 goals?

272. Who scored a brace when The Posh beat Macclesfield 4-0 away during October 2005?

273. Who scored a brace when The Posh beat Bury 3-1 away during April 2006, with Adam Newton scoring the other Peterborough goal?

274. Who started the season as the club's boss but was replaced by Steve Bleasdale in January 2006?

275. Which defender was the only Peterborough player to play in all 46 League matches, scoring 2 goals during the season?

276. Can you name the forward that signed for The Posh during March 2006 from Chesthunt?

277. In what position did The Posh finish in the League – 7th, 8th or 9th?

278. Who scored both goals when The Posh beat Darlington 2-1 at London Road during February 2006?

279. How many of their 46 League matches did Peterborough win?

280. Which Northern Ireland striker scored 7 League goals for The Posh in 21 starts and 3 substitute appearances?

POSITIONS IN DIVISION FOUR

*Match the season/points with the position in which
Peterborough United finished in the League*

281.	1983/1984, 68 points	5th
282.	1973/1974, 65 points	16th
283.	1968/1969, 42 points	7th
284.	1989/1990, 68 points	10th
285.	1971/1972, 50 points	4th
286.	1980/1981, 52 points	11th
287.	1990/1991, 80 points	1st
288.	1986/1987, 65 points	9th
289.	1970/1971, 43 points	18th
290.	1984/1985, 62 points	8th

2004/2005

291. Which team did The Posh beat 1-0 on the opening day of the season, during August 2004, with Sagi Burton scoring the goal?

292. Can you name 2 of the 4 Peterborough scorers in the 4-0 home win against Port Vale during November 2004?

293. True or false: This season was Barry Fry's last in charge at London Road?

294. Which midfielder did the club sign on a free transfer during August 2004 from Nottingham Forest?

295. In what position did The Posh finish in the League – 3rd, 13th or 23rd?

296. Who was the club's highest League scorer with 12 goals?

297. Can you name the 3 goalscorers that scored for The Posh in the 3-0 home win against Hartlepool United on 23 October 2004?

298. How many League goals did Wayne Purser score during this season – 6, 8 or 10?

299. Who scored the only goal in the 1-0 away win against Bournemouth during April 2005?

300. How many of their 46 League games did the club win – 9, 19 or 29?

SQUAD NUMBERS 2008/2009 – 2

Match the player with his squad number for the season

301.	Chris Westwood	2
302.	Paul Coutts	11
303.	Craig Mackail-Smith	18
304.	Aaron McLean	22
305.	Sergio Torres	15
306.	George Boyd	5
307.	Dean Keates	7
308.	Scott Rendell	9
309.	Russell Martin	12
310.	Chris Whelpdale	10

JIM HALL

311.   Jim holds the record for being the club's record League goalscorer, with how many goals?

312.   In which year was Jim born in Northampton –1944, 1945 or 1946?

313.   How many League goals did Jim score during the 1973/1974 season?

314.   True or false: Jim was Peterborough's Player of the Year during the 1974/1975 season?

315.   In what position did Jim play?

316.   Against which club did Jim score 4 League goals, all headers, in September 1973 in a 5-1 home win?

317.   What is Jim's nickname?

318.   Jim scored 2 League goals in a 3-0 home win against Northampton Town in November 1973, a match that attracted the biggest attendance in 8 years. What was the attendance figure - 10,351, 11,351 or 12,351?

319.   How many League appearances did Jim make in the 1974/1975 season, scoring 5 League goals – 23 (1), 25 (1) or 27 (1)?

320.   On 15 December 1973 The Posh beat Wycombe Wanderers 3-1 in the 2nd round of the FA Cup, with Jim scoring in the 72nd minute. Which Peterborough player scored the other 2 goals?

CAPS FOR MY COUNTRY

Match the player with the number of caps
he won for his country

321.   Derek Dougan   5 caps for Wales

322.   Jimmy Rooney   48 caps for Northern Ireland

323.   Dominic Iorfa   39 caps for Northern Ireland

324.   Ken Charlery   99 caps for Australia

325.   Gary Breen   2 caps for Jamaica

326.   Jimmy Quinn   5 caps for St Lucia

327.   David Seaman   21 caps for Nigeria

328.   Steve Morrow   75 caps for England

329.   George Berry   63 caps for Republic of Ireland

330.   Trevor Benjamin   43 caps for Northern Ireland

MATCH THE YEAR – 1

Match up the event with the year it took place

331.	Dominic Green signed for The Posh from Dagenham & Redbridge	1913
332.	Mark Wright took over as The Posh manager	1947
333.	Peter Morris left London Road as manager	2008
334.	Central defender Mick Jones was born	1965
335.	Red-haired goalkeeper Joe Neenan joins Peterborough United	1987
336.	Peterborough were League Two runners-up	1982
337.	Peterborough recorded their record attendance of 30,096 against Swansea Town in the FA Cup	1994
338.	The London Road Stadium was built and opened	2008
339.	Gordon Clarke took over as The Posh boss	2005
340.	Shaun Bradshaw transfers to Blackpool for £35,000.	1964

NATIONALITIES – 2

Match the player with his nationality

341.	Paul Coutts	English
342.	Marcus Ebdon	Northern Irish
343.	David Oldfield	Welsh
344.	David Pleat	Nigerian
345.	James McKeown	Scottish
346.	Simon Davies	Irish Republican
347.	Derek Dougan	Welsh
348.	Dominic Iorfa	English
349.	Ollie Conmy	Australian
350.	David Seaman	Irish Republican

2003/2004

351. In what position did The Posh finish in the League – 16th, 18th or 20th?

352. Who was in charge as manager of The Posh during this season?

353. Which striker did Peterborough sign from Fulham during December 2003?

354. Who scored a brace in the 5-2 home win against Notts County during January 2004?

355. Which midfielder scored 7 League goals in 26 starts and 1 substitute appearance?

356. Against which team did The Posh record their first League win, a 3-0 away win during August 2003 with Andy Clarke, Mark Arber and Andre Boucaud scoring the goals?

357. Who scored a brace in the 4-1 away win during May 2004 against Blackpool?

358. Jason Lee left London Road on 1 August 2003 to join which Scottish team?

359. Who was the club's top goalscorer with 10 League goals?

360. Which team did The Posh beat 6-1 at home during March 2004, with Callum Willock scoring a brace in the game?

HOW MUCH DID THEY PAY? –1

*Match the player with the transfer fee paid
by Peterborough United*

361.	Joe Lewis from Norwich City, 2008	£17,000
362.	Ken Charlery from Birmingham City, 1996	£25,000
363.	Martyn O'Connor from Walsall, 1996	£70,000
364.	Mick Halsall from Grimsby Town, 1987	£400,000
365.	Howard Forinton from Birmingham City, 1999	£40,000
366.	Worrell Sterling from Watford, 1989	£260,000
367.	Pat Gavin from Leicester City, 1991	£350,000
368.	George Boyd from Stevenage Borough, 2007	£150,000
369.	Billy McEwan from Mansfield Town, 1977	£15,000
370.	Joe Cooke from Bradford City, 1979	£250,000

KEN CHARLERY

371. In which year was Ken born – 1962, 1963 or 1964?

372. In what position did Ken play during his playing days?

373. How many spells at the club did Ken have as a player – 3, 4 or 5?

374. Which manager brought Ken to the club for the first time in March 1991?

375. How many League goals did Ken score for Peterborough during his career?

376. Against which team did Ken make his League debut for Peterborough, in a 2-0 home win in March 1991, after coming on as a substitute?

377. How many League goals did Ken score for the club during the 1991/1992 season?

378. Against which team, in a 1-1 away draw during October 1991, did Ken score his first League goal for the club?

379. Ken left London Road in October 1992 and then returned in December 1993, but which team did he play for during his spell away from the club?

380. How many League goals did Ken score for the club in his 19 appearances during the 1995/1996 season?

MATCH THE YEAR – 2

Match up the event with the year it took place

381. **The Posh went 10 hours 55 minutes
     without conceding a goal**   *1984*

382. **The blue and white strip was donate
     to Peterborough by the Supporters' Club**   *1979*

383. **Jim Iley took over as manager of
     Peterborough United**   *1921*

384. **Tommy Robson made his 400th
     League appearances for The Posh**   *1969*

385. **Barry Fry became manager of
     Peterborough United**   *1977*

386. **Peterborough United were relegated
     from Nationwide Division Two**   *1948*

387. **Jack Blood became manager of
     Peterborough United**   *1973*

388. **David Gregory was transferred to
     Stoke City for £55,000**   *1997*

389. **Goalkeeper David Seaman was called
     up for the England Under-21 squad**   *1937*

390. **The Posh nickname for Peterborough
     United was started**   *1996*

2002/2003

391. From which team did Peterborough sign Mark Arber in December 2002?

392. Who was the club's highest League scorer with 16 goals?

393. Which team did The Posh beat 3-2 away on the opening day of the League season during August 2002?

394. Following on from the previous season, which striker scored Peterborough's first goal of the League season?

395. Which team did Peterborough beat 5-1 away from home during March 2003?

396. In what position did The Posh finish in the League – 9th, 11th or 13th?

397. Which defender left London Road to join Hull City in November 2002?

398. Can you name 3 of the 5 goalscorers in the 5-1 home win during September 2002 against Brentford?

399. Which striker scored 5 League goals in 6 starts and 5 substitute appearances?

400. Who was Peterborough's manager during this season?

YEARS AT THE CLUB – 1

*Match the player with the period he spent
at Peterborough United*

401.	David Seaman	2000-03
402.	Jim Hall	1981-84
403.	Tommy Robson	1994-96
404.	Gary Breen	1992-94
405.	Marcus Ebdon	1982-84
406.	Leon McKenzie	1960-62
407.	Terry Bly	1991-97
408.	David Farrell	1968-81
409.	Tony Philliskirk	1997-2006
410.	Colin Clarke	1967-75

1980s

411.   Who managed Peterborough between June 1982 and February 1983?

412.   Who scored 22 League goals in 46 games during 1980/1981?

413.   Who was the club's Player of the Year during 1981/1982?

414.   Can you name the two teams that The Posh beat both home and away in the League during 1986/1987?

415.   True or false: The Posh were unbeaten in their first 10 League games during 1984/1985?

416.   How many of their 46 League games did Peterborough win during 1983/1984 – 18, 19 or 20?

417.   In what position in Division Four did The Posh finish in 1980/1981 and then again in 1981/1982?

418.   Who was the only player to start every League game for The Posh during 1982/1983?

419.   Who scored 22 League goals in 46 games during 1987/1988?

420.   Who managed Peterborough between July 1988 and August 1989?

DIVISION THREE
PLAY-OFF FINAL 1992

421. Which team did Peterborough United beat in the final?

422. Who scored Peterborough's first goal on 52 minutes?

423. Which Peterborough player had the first two shots at goal?

424. Who was the manager of Peterborough United?

425. How many Peterborough United fans travelled to Wembley for the final – 20,000, 25,000 or 30,000?

426. Can you name the Peterborough United substitute, who was the only member of the squad to have played before at Wembley?

427. Ken Charlery scored the winning goal in the 90th minute, a lob over which County goalkeeper?

428. Who was the Posh goalkeeper that wore his trademark 'Old Man' mask when led onto the pitch?

429. What was the final score?

430. On 25 May The Posh players boarded an open-top bus to parade the trophy. How many fans turned out to see them?

MATTHEW ETHERINTON

431. In which year was Matthew born – 1979, 1980 or 1981?

432. How many League goals did Matthew score for Peterborough during his career?

433. Matthew made his debut for Peterborough as a 15-year-old against which team in a 1-0 away win during May 1997?

434. Following on from the previous question, which manager handed Matthew his debut?

435. When Matthew left London Road which London team did he join?

436. How many League goals did Matthew score for The Posh during 1998/1999?

437. Against which team did Matthew score in a 2-0 Peterborough win at London Road during August 1999?

438. How many League appearances did Matthew make for Peterborough during his career – 41, 51 or 61?

439. Against which team did Matthew score in a 4-0 home win during April 1999, with Giuliano Grazioli, Dean Hooper and Francis Green scoring the other goals?

440. Which team did Matthew sign for in August 2003?

HOW MUCH DID THEY PAY? – 2

*Match the player with the transfer fee
paid by Peterborough United*

441. **Phil Crosby from Rotherham United, 1989** £10,000

442. **Fred Barber from Walsall, 1991** £40,000

443. **Ray Hankin from Middlesbrough, 1983** £40,000

444. **Tommy Robson from Newcastle United, 1968** £25,000

445. **Mick Lambert from Ipswich Town, 1979** £100,000

446. **Carl Griffiths from Portsmouth, 1996** £25,000

447. **Danny Carter from Leyton Orient, 1995** £42,500

448. **Paul Culpin from Northampton Town, 1989** £225,000

449. **David Robinson from Halifax Town, 1989** £5,000

450. **Harry Holman from Exeter City, 1978** £20,000

1970s

451. Who took over as manager at Peterborough in May 1977 and managed them until November 1978?

452. Who was the club's Player of the Year during 1973/1974?

453. What was unique about Alan Slough's hat-trick against Chester City during April 1978 in a 4-3 defeat away from home?

454. In what position did The Posh finish during 1976/1977 – 8th, 12th or 16th?

455. By which top-flight team were The Posh defeated 3-1 in the FA Cup 4th round away from home during January 1976, having taken over 10,000 fans to support them?

456. Which team did The Posh beat both at home and away during 1974/1975, although they still went on to win the Division Three title?

457. Can you name one of the three players that played in every League game during 1977/1978?

458. How many players did The Posh use during 1978/1979 – 26, 28 or 30?

459. Which local 17-year-old made his debut during 1976/1977, making 16 League appearances and scoring 3 goals during the season?

460. Which two players finished as the club's highest scorers with only 5 League goals each during 1978/1979?

YEARS AT THE CLUB – 2

*Match the player with the period he spent
at Peterborough United*

461.	Jimmy Bullard	1952-54
462.	Tony Adcock	1963-65
463.	Derek Dougan	2000-02
464.	Andy Clarke	1970-71
465.	David Pleat	1987-88
466.	Fred Barber	1979-83
467.	Paddy Sloan	2001-03
468.	Mickey Gynn	1991-94
469.	Mick Gooding	1999-2005
470.	David Oldfield	1992-94

2001/2002

471. Who was the Peterborough manager during this season?

472. The Posh beat Tranmere Rovers 5-0 at home during March 2002, but which striker scored a hat-trick in the game?

473. Following on from the previous question, who scored a brace in the game, his only League goals for the club during his career?

474. Which team did Peterborough beat 6-0 at home during September 2001?

475. Which London team did The Posh beat 4-1 at home during October 2001, with Neale Fenn scoring a brace?

476. In what position in the League did The Posh finish – 15th, 17th or 19th?

477. Which goalkeeper moved from London Road to sign for Manchester United in May 2002?

478. What was the score when The Posh met Swindon Town on the opening day of the season at the County Ground during August 2001?

479. Can you name the three players that scored against Colchester United in the 3-1 home win during March 2002?

480. Who was the club's highest scorer with 18 League goals in 28 starts and 2 substitute appearances?

POSITIONS THEY PLAYED – 1

Match the player to the position he played

481.	Fred Barber	Defender
482.	Billy McEwan	Winger
483.	Joe Lewis	Outside right
484.	Don Heath	Winger
485.	Ellis Stafford	Goalkeeper
486.	Bobby Barnes	Striker
487.	Sean St Ledger	Goalkeeper
488.	Mike Small	Fullback
489.	Trevor Anderson	Midfield
490.	Bert Murray	Forward

CHRIS TURNER

491.   In what position did Chris play during his playing days?

492.   In which year was Chris born in St Neots – 1951, 1952 or 1953?

493.   When Chris left Peterborough in 1978 which team did he join?

494.   Which team did Chris manage between 1985 and 1990?

495.   How many League goals did Chris score during his career with The Posh – 27, 37 or 47?

496.   How many League goals did Chris score for The Posh during 1973/1974 in his 44 appearances?

497.   Can you name the three managers that Chris played under at London Road?

498.   Chris took over as Peterborough manager in January 1991, but in what year did he leave that position?

499.   Against which team did Chris score a brace in a 4-2 away win during October 1975?

500.   True or false: Chris played in all 46 League games during 1977/1978?

MATCH THE YEAR – 3

Match up the event with the year it took place

501.	Jack Fairbrother took over as manager of Peterborough United	2003
502.	Darragh MacAnthony joined Peterborough United as chairman	1970
503.	Jim Iley signs Richie Barker from Notts County	2000
504.	Bobby Barnes was born	1952
505.	The Posh only played 2 games during February due to the 'big freeze'	1962
506.	Percy Allen was born	1998
507.	Jimmy Bullard joined Wigan Athletic	1947
508.	David Pleat joined Peterborough United	1971
509.	Jimmy Quinn scored his 25th and last League goal for The Posh	1895
510.	Simon Davies joined Tottenham Hotspur for £700,000	2006

HAT-TRICKS

*Match up the fixture with the player who scored
a hat-trick for Peterborough*

511. v. Brentford (home),
     November 2007, League   **Alan Slough**

512. v. Hull City (away),
     November 1995, League   **John Cozens**

513. v. Oxford United (home),
     September 1993, League   **Aaron McLean**

514. v. Gillingham (away),
     November 1988, FA Cup 1st round   **Robbie Cooke**

515. v. Newport County (away),
     April 1988, League   **Gary Martindale**

516. v. Accrington Stanley (home),
     January 2008, League   **Craig Mackail-Smith**

517. v. Portsmouth (home),
     January 1977, League   **Steve Phillips**

518. v. Chester City (away),
     April 1978, League   **Tony Philliskirk**

519. v. Hartlepool United (home),
     February 1982, League   **Aaron McLean**

520. v. Staines (away),
     December 2007, FA Cup 2nd round   **Dave Longhurst**

POSITIONS THEY PLAYED – 2

Match the player with the position he played

521.	David Farrell	Goalkeeper
522.	Gordon Pulley	Centre back
523.	Jim Walker	Winger
524.	Mark Tyler	Striker
525.	Mark Peters	Midfield
526.	Archie Styles	Goalkeeper
527.	George Berry	Left back
528.	Paul Price	Fullback
529.	Aaron McLean	Defender
530.	Jon Sheffield	Central defender

2000/2001

531. Who scored the goal on the opening day of the season in the 1-0 away win against Oxford United during August 2000?

532. In what position in the League did The Posh finish – 12th, 16th or 20th?

533. Which striker did Peterborough sign on a free transfer from Crystal Palace during October 2000?

534. Which striker did The Posh sell to Kidderminster during February 2001?

535. Which team did The Posh beat 4-1 at home during March 2001?

536. Can you name the 2 players that scored for The Posh in the 2-0 home win against Walsall during April 2001?

537. The Posh beat Wycombe 3-2 at London Road during February 2001 after being 2-0 down after 14 minutes. Who scored the winning goal in the 34th minute?

538. How many points did the club win in the League – 49, 59 or 69?

539. Which striker scored 7 League goals during the season in his 14 starts and 16 substitute appearances?

540. How many of their 46 League games did Peterborough win – 15, 25 or 35?

DEREK DOUGAN

541. Derek was born in Belfast on 20 January in which year
     – 1934, 1936 or 1938?

542. How many appearances did Derek make at
     international level for Northern Ireland?

543. From which club did Derek join The Posh in 1963?

544. Which honour did Derek win with Wolverhampton
     Wanderers in 1974?

545. How many League appearances did Derek make for
     Peterborough United – 67, 77 or 87?

546. In 1954 Derek started his career with Distillery before
     moving to Portsmouth in August 1957, for what
     transfer fee?

547. Which club did Derek join in March 1959 for £15,000?

548. How many League goals did Derek score for The Posh?

549. In March 1967 Derek moved from which club to
     Wolverhampton Wanderers for £50,000?

550. In 1969 Derek won the NASL International Cup with
     which American club?

BIG WINS

Match up the fixture with Peterborough's high-scoring victory

551. v. Brentford (home),
      November 2007, League   **5-0**

552. v. Hartlepool United (home),
      October 2004, League   **6-0**

553. v. Notts County (home),
      January 2004, League   **6-1**

554. v. Rotherham (home),
      November 1996, League   **7-0**

555. v. Torquay United (home),
      November 2006, League   **4-1**

556. v. Oldham Athletic (away),
      August 2000, League   **8-2**

557. v. Accrington Stanley (home),
      January 2008, League   **5-2**

558. v. Wrexham (home),
      March 2004, League   **5-2**

559. v. Bournemouth (home),
      September 2001, League   **6-2**

560. v. Tranmere Rovers (home),
      March 2002, League   **3-0**

DAVID SEAMAN

561. David was born on19 September 1963 in which Yorkshire town?

562. Which honour was David awarded in 1997 for his services to sport?

563. Which club did David transfer to in August 1986 for £225,000?

564. At which club did David start his professional football career in 1982?

565. In October 1984 David joined Birmingham City, for what transfer fee - £75,000, £100,000 or £125,000?

566. David made his England debut in a friendly against Saudi Arabia in November 1988, under which England manager?

567. How many League appearances did David make for Peterborough United?

568. Which club paid £1.3 million for David's services in 1990, where he went on to make 405 League appearances?

569. At which club did David play at youth level in 1981?

570. Between 1988 and 2002 how many appearances did David make at international level for England?

LEAGUE GOALS DURING 2007/2008

Match up the player with the number of League goals scored

571.	Chris Whelpdale	29
572.	Scott Rendell	12
573.	Danny Crow	12
574.	Dean Keates	6
575.	Rene Howe	5
576.	Aaron McLean	3
577.	George Boyd	3
578.	Charlie Lee	2
579.	Craig Mackail-Smith	2
580.	Craig Morgan	1

ADAM DRURY

581. Adam was born in Cottenham on 29 August in which year – 1974, 1976 or 1978?

582. At which club did Adam start his professional football career in 1995?

583. In March 2001 Adam was transferred for £500,000 to which club?

584. In what position does Adam play?

585. How many League appearances did Adam make for Peterborough United – 128 (10), 138 (10) or 148 (10)?

586. In what year did Adam win the Championship with Norwich City?

587. How many League goals did Adam score for The Posh?

588. Who was manager at Peterborough United when Adam left the club in 2001?

589. In July 2000 which club made an offer to Peterborough for Adam's services but were turned down?

590. Adam made his first full League appearance for The Posh in 1996 away at which club?

JIMMY QUINN

591. In what year did Jimmy sign for The Posh?

592. Against which team did Jimmy make his Posh League debut in a 1-0 home defeat?

593. How many League goals did Jimmy score during his Peterborough career – 25, 30 or 35?

594. True or false: Jimmy scored 20 League goals in his 40 starts and 2 substitute appearances during his first season at the club?

595. Jimmy scored a hat-trick in only his 6th League match for The Posh, against which team in a 5-1 home win?

596. Which manager signed Jimmy for The Posh?

597. Against which team did Jimmy score his first goal of the 1998/1999 season?

598. For which country has Jimmy won full international caps?

599. Against which team did Jimmy score a brace during September 1998 in a 4-1 League win?

600. How many League goals did Jimmy score in his 7 starts during 1998/1999?

TONY ADCOCK

601. Tony was born in Bethnal Green on 27 February in which year – 1963, 1965 or 1967?

602. In what position does Tony play?

603. At which club did Tony start his professional football career in March 1981, where he has made 318 League appearances in two spells there?

604. On 7 November 1987 Tony scored a hat-trick for Manchester City in a 10-1 win over Huddersfield Town, but which other two players also scored hat-tricks in this game?

605. Tony joined Peterborough United in February 1992 along with Bobby Barnes, but from which club did they both sign?

606. How many League appearances did Tony make for The Posh – 107 (4), 117 (4) or 127 (4)?

607. On 6 October 1989 Tony was transferred to Bradford City, for what fee?

608. In January 1988 Tony transferred for £85,000 to which club?

609. How many League goals did Tony score for Peterborough United in his two years with the club?

610. In 1999 Tony played for which non-League club?

HIGHEST LEAGUE GOALSCORERS – 1

Match up the season with the player that scored the highest number of League goals

611.	1978/1979	Jackie Gallacher (12 goals)
612.	1979/1980	Errington Kelly (11 goals)
613.	1980/1981	Billy Kellock (19 goals)
614.	1981/1982	Steve Phillips (11 goals)
615.	1982/1983	Robbie Cooke (22 goals)
616.	1983/1984	Barry Butlin and Joe Cooke (5 goals)
617.	1984/1985	Robbie Cooke (24 goals)
618.	1985/1986	Mick Gooding (18 goals)
619.	1986/1987	Alan Waddle (12 goals)
620.	1987/1988	Mickey Gynn (17 goals)

DAVID FARRELL

621.   David was born on 11 November 1971 in which
        Midlands city?

622.   David began his professional career at which non-
        League club in 1991?

623.   David joined Wycombe Wanderers in 1995, for what
        transfer fee - £75,000, £100,000 or £125,000?

624.   Which club did David join in 1992 for £45,000?

625.   How many League appearances did David make for
        The Posh – 175 (21), 185 (21) or 195 (21)?

626.   In what position does David play?

627.   In June 2006 David joined which club on a free
        transfer from Peterborough?

628.   How many League goals did David score during his
        nine years at Peterborough United?

629.   In 1993 David had a loan spell at which club but never
        played a game?

630.   For which Conference club did David play in
        2007-2008, making 17 (4) appearances?

AGAINST WHICH TEAM?

631. *Which team did The Posh beat 1-0 in the play-off final during May 2000?*

632. *Which team did Peterborough play on the opening day of the 1998/1999 season?*

633. *Which team did The Posh beat 4-2 at London Road on 1 May 1974?*

634. *Which team did Peterborough beat 5-1, with Jimmy Quinn scoring a hat-trick, during September 1997?*

635. *Which team did Peterborough play on the opening day of the 1979/1980 season?*

636. *Which team defeated The Posh 6-0 in the League Cup 2nd round, 1st leg, during September 1995?*

637. *Which team defeated The Posh 5-4 in the League during January 1996?*

638. *Which team did Peterborough play on the opening day of the 1987/1988 season?*

639. *Which team did The Posh beat 5-1, with Martin Carruthers scoring a brace, during December 1997?*

640. *Which team did Peterborough play on the opening day of the 1974/1975 season?*

MARK TYLER

641.   Mark was born on 2 April 1997 in which city?

642.   In what position does Mark play?

643.   In which tournament did Mark win his first England Under-20 cap in 1997?

644.   In 1996 at which Isthmian League Premier Division club did Mark have a loan spell, making four League appearances?

645.   At which club did Mark start his professional football career in 1994?

646.   Mark was loaned out by Peterborough United from January to March 2008 to which Championship club?

647.   Mark made his debut for Peterborough on 18 September 1994 in a League One away match that ended in a 4-0 defeat to which opponents?

648.   In October 1999 which were the only team to put a goal past Mark at London Road?

649.   In January 1999 Mark was injured in a home match against Hull City and was replaced in the next game against Brighton & Hove Albion by which player making his Posh debut?

650.   In 1994 which goalkeeper did Mark replace at Peterborough United?

NOEL CANTWELL

651.   What nationality was Noel?

652.   In what position did Noel play during his playing days
       – fullback, midfielder or inside forward?

653.   In what year did Noel take over as Peterborough
       manager?

654.   True or false: Noel was also a professional cricket
       player?

655.   In what position in the League did Noel guide The
       Posh during 1974/1975 in Division Three?

656.   Which team did Noel manage between October 1967
       and March 1972?

657.   Noel returned for a second spell in charge of The Posh,
       in which year?

658.   Following on from the previous question, which team
       did Peterborough play for his first game back in
       charge, a 1-1 draw away from home?

659.   Which manager took over at the club when Noel left in
       1988?

660.   In what position in the League did Noel guide The
       Posh during 1987/1988 in Division Four?

PLAYER OF THE YEAR

Match the player with the year he was awarded Player of the Year

661.	Ian Bennett	1988
662.	Tommy Robson	1995
663.	Adam Drury	1974
664.	Bob Doyle	2000
665.	Andy Clarke	1990
666.	Mick Gooding	1980
667.	Dave Longhurst	1979
668.	Dave Robinson	1998
669.	Billy Kellock	1993
670.	Ken Charlery	1989

ANDY CLARKE

671. For which London team did Andy play between February 1991 and May 1999?

672. Against which team did Andy make his League debut for Peterborough in a 3-1 away defeat, having come on as a substitute?

673. Andy scored his first goal for The Posh in the FA Cup, against which team in the 1st round at London Road?

674. How many League goals did Andy score for The Posh during his career – 37, 47 or 57?

675. In what year did Andy sign for The Posh?

676. True or false: Andy scored the only goal in the 1-0 play-off final match at Wembley in 2000 against Darlington?

677. How many League goals did Andy score in his first season at The Posh – 13, 14 or 15?

678. Which Peterborough manager brought Andy to the club?

679. Andy scored his last Peterborough goal during October 2004 against which team in a 1-1 home draw?

680. How many League appearances did Andy make for Peterborough in his career – 230, 235 or 240?

WORRELL STERLING

681.   Worrell was born on 8 June 1965 in which part of East London?

682.   On 8 April 1989 Worrell scored his first goal for The Posh in a 3-1 home win against which club?

683.   At which club in 1983 did Worrell start his professional career?

684.   What was Worrell's transfer fee when he joined Peterborough United from Watford in 1989?

685.   How many League appearances did Worrell make for The Posh – 170 (3), 180 (3) or 190 (3)?

686.   Worrell made his debut for which club on 16 August 1997 at home against Northwich Victoria, a game that was also to be his last for the club?

687.   In the 1989/1990 season how many League games did Worrell play for The Posh?

688.   Which West Country club did Worrell join for £140,000 on 29 July 1993?

689.   In what position did Worrell play?

690.   How many League goals did Worrell score in his four seasons at Peterborough United – 18, 28 or 38?

UNUSUAL RESULTS

Match up the fixture with the final score

691. *v. Hartlepool United (home),*
      September 2006, League   **9-1**

692. *v. Peterborough (away),*
      March 2005, League   **6-3**

693. *v. Exeter City (home),*
      October 1989, League   **3-4**

694. *v. Bristol Rovers (home),*
      September 2008, League   **0-5**

695. *v. Wycombe Wanderers (home),*
      September 1996, League   **3-5**

696. *v. Chelsea (away),*
      January 2001, FA Cup 3rd round   **0-4**

697. *v. Brighton & Hove Albion (away),*
      November 1999, FA Cup 1st round replay   **4-3**

698. *v. Stoke City (home),*
      February 2001, League   **0-5**

699. *v. Barnet (away),*
      September 1998, League   **5-4**

700. *v. Hartlepool United (home),*
      August 2003, League   **0-3**

POT LUCK

701. Who was Player of the Year for Peterborough United in 1981?

702. On Boxing Day 1999 which club beat Peterborough at home 5-0?

703. In how many League games did The Posh draw in the 1989/1990 season, the most in Division Four?

704. In the 1991/1992 season how many consecutive League wins did Peterborough United have?

705. At the beginning of the 1992/1993 season what was the price of a terrace ticket at London Road - £8, £9 or £10?

706. Between September 1978 and January 1979 The Posh went how many League matches without a win?

707. In the 1984/1985 season which player was Peterborough's top goalscorer in all competitions, with 14 goals?

708. Which player scored two hat-tricks for The Posh in the 1981/1982 season?

709. How many League goals did Peterborough United score in the 1977/1978 season – 37, 47 or 57?

710. On 29 April 1978 which player scored a hat-trick of penalties against Chester City away?

FOURTH DIVISION CHAMPIONSHIP
– 1973/1974

711.   Who was Peterborough's manager during this success?

712.   How many of their 46 League matches did the club win?

713.   Who was the club's Player of the Year during this season?

714.   How many players were used during this season – 19, 20 or 21?

715.   Who was the club's highest League scorer, with 19 goals in 46 League appearances?

716.   Which team did the club beat 2-1 on the opening day of the season?

717.   Which player scored 4 goals for The Posh in a 5-1 home win during September 1973?

718.   Was this the 2nd, 3rd or 4th time in the club's history that they had won the Fourth Division Championship?

719.   True or false: the club were unbeaten at home in the League throughout the whole season?

720.   Can you name the three players that scored in the 3-2 home win on New Year's Day 1974?

APPEARANCES FOR THE CLUB

Match the player with the number of appearances
he made in all competitions for Peterborough United

721.	Mick Halsall	196
722.	Tommy Robson	394 (26)
723.	Noel Luke	212
724.	Chris Turner	316 (1)
725.	Jack Carmichael	207 (23)
726.	Worrell Sterling	336 (10)
727.	Peter McNamee	234 (3)
728.	Jim Hall	357 (7)
729.	David Farrell	514 (45)
730.	John Crawford	329 (5)

AARON McLEAN

731. From which team did The Posh sign Aaron on New Year's Day 2007?

732. Following on from the previous question, how much did Peterborough pay for Aaron?

733. True or false: Aaron was named in the PFA League Two Team of the Year 2008?

734. Against which team did Aaron score his first League goal of the 2008/2009 season in a 3-0 home win during August 2008?

735. For which London club did Aaron play between 1999 and 2003?

736. In what position does Aaron play?

737. How many hat-tricks did Aaron score for Peterborough during 2007/2008?

738. Following on from the previous question, can you name the opponents?

739. Against which team did Aaron score a brace during April 2008 in a 4-1 away win?

740. In what year did Aaron initially sign for The Posh on loan?

TOMMY ROBSON

741. Tommy was born on 31 July 1944 in which north-east town?

742. In which year did Tommy join Peterborough United – 1968, 1969 or 1970?

743. From which club did Tommy sign to join The Posh?

744. In the 1973/1974 season Tommy and which two other players made 46 League appearances for The Posh?

745. Tommy was Peterborough's top League goalscorer in the 1977/1978 season, with how many goals?

746. How many League goals did Tommy score for The Posh – 101, 111 or 121?

747. At which club did Tommy make his professional debut in 1961?

748. How many League appearances did Tommy make for The Posh – 440 (42), 450 (42) or 460 (42)?

749. Tommy scored a hat-trick on 19 April 1975 in a 3-0 away win against which club?

750. Tommy won Player of the Year for the second time at Peterborough in which year – 1978, 1979 or 1980?

HIGHEST LEAGUE GOALSCORERS – 2

*Match up the season with the player that scored
the highest number of League goals*

751.	1988/1989	Tony Adcock (12 goals)
752.	1989/1990	Ken Charlery (16 goals)
753.	1990/1991	Scott Houghton (8 goals)
754.	1991/1992	Jimmy Quinn (20 goals)
755.	1992/1993	Mick Halsall (11 goals)
756.	1993/1994	Ken Charlery (16 goals)
757.	1994/1995	Nick Cusack (10 goals)
758.	1995/1996	Tony Adcock (16 goals)
759.	1996/1997	Paul Culpin (10 goals)
760.	1997/1998	Gary Martindale (15 goals)

CLUB GOALSCORERS

*Match up the player with the numbers of goals scored
in all competitions for Peterborough United*

761.	Worrell Sterling	43
762.	Jim Hall	68
763.	Andy Clarke	39
764.	Chris Turner	38
765.	Tommy Robson	80
766.	Terry Bly	42
767.	Peter McNamee	137
768.	Leon McKenzie	27
769.	Ken Charlery	128
770.	Tony Adcock	87

GEORGE BOYD

771.   In what year did George sign for The Posh on New Year's Day?

772.   In what position does George play – defender, midfielder or striker?

773.   From which team did George sign to join The Posh?

774.   Which team were Peterborough playing when George made his debut in a 3-1 away defeat, with Adam Smith scoring for The Posh?

775.   True or false: George scored his first League goals for The Posh against Wrexham in a 3-0 home win during February 2007?

776.   How many League goals did George score for The Posh in his first season at the club?

777.   Against which team did George score a hat-trick for The Posh during January 2008 in a 8-2 home League win?

778.   How many League goals did George score during 2007/2008 for Peterborough?

779.   In which year was George born – 1984, 1985 or 1986?

780.   In which competition were the club playing when George scored the winning goal in a 3-2 away win against Nottingham Forest during September 2007?

TERRY BLY

781.   Terry was born in Fincham on 22 October in which year
       – 1931, 1933 or 1935?

782.   In what position did Terry play?

783.   From which club did Terry join Peterborough United in
       1960?

784.   How many League goals did Terry score in the Division
       Four season of 1960/1961 – 32, 42 or 52?

785.   In his two seasons at Peterborough how many League
       appearances did Terry make?

786.   In 1962 Terry left The Posh to join which club for a
       season, making 32 League appearances and scoring 25
       goals?

787.   Which non-League club did Terry join in October 1964,
       where he made 199 appearances and scored 125
       goals?

788.   How many League goals did Terry score for
       Peterborough United?

789.   In which year did Terry retire from playing football –
       1970, 1972 or 1974?

790.   Terry went on to manage Grantham Town until 1978,
       where he won over half of his games. For how many
       games was he in charge, a club record?

HIGHEST LEAGUE GOALSCORERS – 3

Match up the season with the player that scored the highest number of League goals

791.	1998/1999	Aaron McLean (29 goals)
792.	1999/2000	Leon McKenzie (10 goals)
793.	2000/2001	Callum Willock (12 goals)
794.	2001/2002	Andy Clarke (16 goals)
795.	2002/2003	Danny Crow (15 goals)
796.	2003/2004	Giuliano Grazioli (15 goals)
797.	2004/2005	Craig Mackail-Smith (8 goals)
798.	2005/2006	Leon McKenzie (18 goals)
799.	2006/2007	Leon McKenzie (13 goals)
800.	2007/2008	Andy Clarke (15 goals)

ANSWERS

HISTORY OF THE CLUB

1.   1934 (17 May)
2.   The Posh
3.   London Road Stadium
4.   Peterborough & Fletton United
5.   1960
6.   Gateshead FC
7.   Sam Madden (1938-48) and Barry Fry (1996-2005)
8.   Northampton Town and Cambridge United
9.   Terry Bly
10.   Sir Alex Ferguson

WHO AM I? – 1

11.   Craig Mackail-Smith
12.   Joe Lewis
13.   Jimmy Quinn
14.   Chris Westwood
15.   Gabriel Zakuani
16.   Terry Bly
17.   John Barnwell
18.   Nick Cusack
19.   Ian Bennett
20.   Wakeley Gage

CLUB RECORDS

21.   Jim Hall
22.   Swansea Town
23.   134
24.   Rushden Town 1-9 Peterborough United
25.   J. Laxton
26.   482 (42)
27.   Simon Davies
28.   Walsall
29.   Mick Drewery
30.   Barnet

THE LEAGUE CUP

31.   Southampton

32. *Ipswich Town*

33. *Trevor Benjamin and Guy Branson*

34. *David Gregory*

35. *Fulham (2-1 win away and 2-0 win at home)*

36. *Portsmouth*

37. *Robbie Cooke*

38. *George Boyd*

39. *Swansea City*

40. *Billy Manuel*

CLUB HONOURS

41.	*Division Four Champions (first time)*	*1961*
42.	*League Cup semi-finalists*	*1966*
43.	*Finished 10th in Division One*	*1993*
44.	*Promoted to Division Two via play-offs (second time)*	*2000*
45.	*Division Four champions (second time)*	*1974*
46.	*Promoted to Division Three*	*1991*
47.	*Promoted to Division Two via play-offs (first time)*	*1992*
48.	*League Two runners-up*	*2008*
49.	*Reached the 6th round of the FA Cup*	*1965*
50.	*Midland League champions (first time)*	*1956*

SIMON DAVIES

51. *1979*

52. *6*

53. *Welsh*

54. *16*

55. *Matthew Etherington*

56. *Fulham*

57. *Hull City*

58. *4*

59. *Southend United*

60. *Giuliano Grazioli and Scott Houghton*

WHERE DID THEY GO? – 1

61.	*George Berry*	*Preston North End*
62.	*Jimmy Bullard*	*Wigan Athletic*

63.	Adam Newton	Brentford
64.	David Seaman	Birmingham City
65.	David Rogers	Carlisle United
66.	George Swindin	Arsenal
67.	Adam Drury	Norwich City
68.	Matthew Etherington	Tottenham Hotspur
69.	Simon Yeo	Chester City
70.	Alan Waddle	Hartlepool United

2008/2009

71. Darren Ferguson
72. Leyton Orient
73. Bristol Rovers
74. Craig Mackail-Smith
75. 21
76. MK Dons
77. Dominic Green
78. George Boyd and Craig Mackail-Smith
79. 7
80. Tranmere Rovers

MANAGERS – 1

81.	Peter Morris	1979-82
82.	Jack Fairbrother	1962-64
83.	John Wile	1983-86
84.	John Still	1994-95
85.	Keith Alexander	2006-07
86.	Jock Porter	1934-36
87.	Noel Cantwell	1972-77
88.	Mark Lawrenson	1989-90
89.	Norman Rigby	1967-69
90.	Bob Gurney	1950-52

2007/2008

91. Darren Ferguson
92. Brentford
93. Aaron McLean
94. Aaron McLean and Scott Rendell

95.	Rochdale
96.	2nd
97.	Aaron McLean
98.	George Boyd and Craig Mackail-Smith
99.	Dean Keates
100.	Jeff Hughes

NATIONALITIES – 1

101.	Sergio Torres	Argentinean
102.	Aidy Boothroyd	English
103.	Tom Williams	English-Cypriot
104.	Micah Hyde	Jamaican
105.	Jimmy Rooney	Australian
106.	Ken Charlery	St Lucian
107.	Craig Morgan	Welsh
108.	Gary Breen	Irish Republican
109.	Jimmy Bullard	English
110.	Dick Whittaker	Irish Republican

WHO AM I? – 2

111.	Peter Deakin
112.	Frank Rankmore
113.	David Langan
114.	John Crawford
115.	Eric Steele
116.	Mick Gooding
117.	Garry Butterworth
118.	George Boyd
119.	Micah Hyde
120.	Lil Fuccillo

WHERE DID THEY COME FROM? – 1

121.	George Boyd	Stevenage Borough
122.	Derek Dougan	Aston Villa
123.	Clive Platt	Notts County
124.	Chris Westwood	Walsall
125.	Tim Ryan	Doncaster Rovers
126.	Danny Crow	Norwich City

127.	Bradley Allen	Grimsby Town
128.	Liam Hatch	Barnet
129.	Willie Duff	Charlton Athletic
130.	Aidy Boothroyd	Mansfield Town

DEBUTS

131.	v. Rochdale (home), August 2007, 3-0 League win	Dean Keates
132.	v. Southend United (away), August 2008, 1-0 League defeat	Sergio Torres
133.	v. Bristol Rovers (away), August 1996, 1-0 League defeat	Roger Willis
134.	v. Southend United (home), October 1999, 1-0 League win	Grant Haley
135.	v. Tranmere Rovers (home), August 1984, 1-0 League win	David Johnson
136.	v. Lincoln City (away), August 1979, 1-0 League win	Ricky Heppolette
137.	v. Bristol Rovers (away), August 1996, 1-0 League defeat	Scott Houghton
138.	v. Southend United (home), January 1993, 1-0 League win	John McGlashan
139.	v. Bristol Rovers (away), February 2007, 3-2 League defeat	Shane Blackett
140.	v. Bristol Rovers (away), August 1996, 1-0 League defeat	Martin O'Connor

POSITIONS IN LEAGUE TWO

141.	1994/1995, 60 points	15th
142.	2007/2008, 92 points	2nd
143.	2003/2004, 52 points	18th
144.	1995/1996, 52 points	19th
145.	2000/2001, 59 points	12th
146.	2006/2007, 65 points	10th
147.	2001/2002, 55 points	17th
148.	1996/1997, 47 points	21st
149.	2002/2003, 58 points	11th
150.	2005/2006, 62 points	9th

BARRY FRY

151. **Francis**
152. **Inside forward**
153. **Southend United**
154. **1996**
155. **Mick Halsall**
156. **Bristol Rovers (August 1996)**
157. **True**
158. **5th**
159. **2005**
160. **Manchester United**

POSITIONS IN LEAGUE THREE

161.	1999/2000, 78 points	5th
162.	1962/1963, 51 points	6th
163.	1976/1977, 41 points	16th
164.	1997/1998, 67 points	10th
165.	1964/1965, 51 points	8th
166.	1966/1967, 43 points	15th
167.	1974/1975, 50 points	7th
168.	1998/1999, 66 points	9th
169.	1977/1978, 56 points	4th
170.	1978/1979, 36 points	21st

2006/2007

171. **Bristol Rovers**
172. **70 (48 at home and 22 away)**
173. **10th**
174. **18**
175. **Craig Mackail-Smith**
176. **Torquay United**
177. **George Boyd**
178. **Peter Gain, Gavin Strachan, Craig Mackail-Smith and Richard Butcher**
179. **True: 3 wins and 2 draws**
180. **10 February 2007**

SQUAD NUMBERS 2008/2009 – 1

181.	Craig Morgan	4
182.	James McKeown	13
183.	Charlie Lee	6
184.	Jamie Day	17
185.	Dominic Green	25
186.	Micah Hyde	8
187.	Joe Lewis	1
188.	Tom Williams	21
189.	Mark Tyler	34
190.	Shane Blackett	3

GOALKEEPERS

191.	Joe Lewis
192.	Mark Tyler
193.	Eric Steele
194.	Wrexham
195.	Martin Wilkinson
196.	Paul Bradshaw (39 games) and Kevin Dearden (7)
197.	Ian Bennett
198.	Jim Barron
199.	Kevin Shoemaker (34 games), Andy Beasley (7 games), Paul Crichton (4 games) and John Smeulders (1 game)
200.	Keith Waugh

WHERE DID THEY GO? – 2

201.	Bryn Gunn	Chesterfield
202.	Pat Gavin	Northampton Town
203.	Ray Hankin	Wolverhampton Wanderers
204.	Craig Allardyce	Welling United
205.	Martin Carruthers	Darlington
206.	Jimmy Quinn	Swindon Town
207.	Curtis Woodhouse	Hull City
208.	Lee Power	Dundee
209.	Trevor Whymark	Colchester United
210.	Gordon Polley	Chelmsford City

DARREN FERGUSON

211.	1972
212.	Manchester United
213.	2007
214.	March
215.	Wrexham
216.	Tom Williams, Russell Martin and Sergio Torres
217.	10th
218.	28
219.	Wolverhampton Wanderers
220.	Midfield

MANAGERS – 2

221.	Barry Fry	1996-2005
222.	John Barnwell	1977-78
223.	Jimmy Hagan	1958-62
224.	Mark Wright	2005-06
225.	Sam Madden	1938-48
226.	Jim Iley	1969-72
227.	Mick Jones	1988-89
228.	Mick Halsall	1995-96
229.	Steve Bleasdale	2006
230.	George Swindin	1954-58

JIMMY BULLARD

231.	Midfield (central)
232.	2001
233.	West Ham United
234.	Barry Fry
235.	Bournemouth
236.	11
237.	Wigan Athletic
238.	1-1
239.	Andy Clarke
240.	8

WHERE DID THEY COME FROM? – 2

241.	Danny Blanchett	Cambridge City

242.	Miguel de Souza	Wycombe Wanderers
243.	Gary Breen	Gillingham
244.	Jim Baron	Connecticut Bicentennials
245.	Ernie Moss	Chesterfield
246.	Simon Rea	Birmingham City
247.	Trevor Benjamin	Coventry City
248.	Ron Barnes	Norwich City
249.	Paul Bradshaw	West Bromwich Albion
250.	Charlie Lee	Tottenham Hotspur

1990s

251.	1994
252.	Tony Adcock
253.	True
254.	4th
255.	Wayne Andrews
256.	36
257.	Chris Turner
258.	Steve Welsh
259.	Northampton Town
260.	Liverpool

FA CUP WINS

261.	2007/2008, 3rd round	Colchester United 1-3 Peterborough United
262.	1982/1983, 2nd round	Peterborough United 5-2 Doncaster Rovers
263.	1969/1970, 3rd round	Rotherham United 0-1 Peterborough United
264.	1980/1981, 4th round	Notts County 0-1 Peterborough United
265.	2003/2004, 2nd round	Peterborough United 3-2 Grimsby Town
266.	1970/1971, 1st round	Peterborough United 3-1 Wimbledon
267.	1964/1965, 4th round	Peterborough United 2-1 Arsenal

268.	1960/1961, 3rd round	Portsmouth 1-2 Peterborough United
269.	1973/1974, 3rd round	Peterborough United 3-1 Southend United
270.	1996/1997, 3rd round	Plymouth Argyle 0-1 Peterborough United

2005/2006

271. Danny Crow
272. David Farrell
273. Danny Crow
274. Mark Wright
275. Mark Arber
276. Lloyd Opara
277. 9th
278. Mark Arber
279. 17
280. James Quinn

POSITIONS IN DIVISION FOUR

281.	1983/1984, 68 points	7th
282.	1973/1974, 65 points	1st
283.	1968/1969, 42 points	18th
284.	1989/1990, 68 points	9th
285.	1971/1972, 50 points	8th
286.	1980/1981, 52 points	5th
287.	1990/1991, 80 points	4th
288.	1986/1987, 65 points	10th
289.	1970/1971, 43 points	16th
290.	1984/1985, 62 points	11th

2004/2005

291. Tranmere Rovers
292. Wayne Purser, David Farrell, Andre Boucaud and Curtis Woodhouse
293. True
294. Danny Sonner
295. 23rd

296. *Callum Willock*

297. *Peter Kennedy, Callum Willock and Andy Legg*

298. *6*

299. *Callum Willock*

300. *9*

SQUAD NUMBERS 2008/2009 – 2

301.	Chris Westwood	5
302.	Paul Coutts	15
303.	Craig Mackail-Smith	12
304.	Aaron McLean	9
305.	Sergio Torres	22
306.	George Boyd	10
307.	Dean Keates	11
308.	Scott Rendell	7
309.	Russell Martin	2
310.	Chris Whelpdale	18

JIM HALL

311. *122*

312. *1945*

313. *13*

314. *False: the award was won by Jack Carmichael*

315. *Centre forward*

316. *Doncaster Rovers*

317. *Big Jim*

318. *10,351*

319. *25 (1)*

320. *John Cozens (35th and 62nd minutes)*

CAPS FOR MY COUNTRY

321.	Derek Dougan	43 caps for Northern Ireland
322.	Jimmy Rooney	99 caps for Australia
323.	Dominic Iorfa	21 caps for Nigeria
324.	Ken Charlery	5 caps for St Lucia
325.	Gary Breen	63 caps for Republic of Ireland
326.	Jimmy Quinn	48 caps for Northern Ireland
327.	David Seaman	75 caps for England

328.	Steve Morrow	39 caps for Northern Ireland
329.	George Berry	5 caps for Wales
330.	Trevor Benjamin	2 caps for Jamaica

MATCH THE YEAR – 1

331.	Dominic Green signed for The Posh from Dagenham & Redbridge	2008
332.	Mark Wright took over as The Posh manager	2005
333.	Peter Morris left London Road as manager	1982
334.	Central defender Mick Jones was born	1947
335.	Red-haired goalkeeper Joe Neenan joins Peterborough United	1987
336.	Peterborough were League Two runners-up	2008
337.	Peterborough recorded their record attendance of 30,096 against Swansea Town in the FA Cup	1965
338.	The London Road Stadium was built and opened	1913
339.	Gordon Clarke took over as The Posh boss	1964
340.	Shaun Bradshaw transfers to Blackpool for £35,000	1994

NATIONALITIES – 2

341.	Paul Coutts	Scottish
342.	Marcus Ebdon	Welsh
343.	David Oldfield	Australian
344.	David Pleat	English
345.	James McKeown	Irish Republican
346.	Simon Davies	Welsh
347.	Derek Dougan	Northern Irish
348.	Dominic Iorfa	Nigerian
349.	Ollie Conmy	Irish Republican
350.	David Seaman	English

2003/2004

351.	18th
352.	Barry Fry
353.	Callum Willock
354.	Richard Logan
355.	Curtis Woodhouse

356. **Brentford**

357. **Curtis Woodhouse**

358. **Falkirk**

359. **Leon McKenzie**

360. **Wrexham**

HOW MUCH DID THEY PAY? –1

361.	Joe Lewis from Norwich City, 2008	£400,000
362.	Ken Charlery from Birmingham City, 1996	£150,000
363.	Martyn O'Connor from Walsall, 1996	£350,000
364.	Mick Halsall from Grimsby Town, 1987	£25,000
365.	Howard Forinton from Birmingham City, 1999	£250,000
366.	Worrell Sterling from Watford, 1989	£70,000
367.	Pat Gavin from Leicester City, 1991	£15,000
368.	George Boyd from Stevenage Borough, 2007	£260,000
369.	Billy McEwan from Mansfield Town, 1977	£17,000
370.	Joe Cooke from Bradford City, 1979	£40,000

KEN CHARLERY

371. **1964**

372. **Striker**

373. **3**

374. **Chris Turner**

375. **55**

376. **Blackpool**

377. **16**

378. **Reading**

379. **Watford**

380. **7**

MATCH THE YEAR – 2

381.	The Posh went 10 hours 55 minutes without conceding a goal	1973
382.	The blue and white strip was donated to Peterborough by the Supporters' Club	1937
383.	Jim Iley took over as manager of Peterborough United	1969
384.	Tommy Robson made his 400th League	

	appearances for The Posh	1979
385.	Barry Fry became manager of Peterborough United	1996
386.	Peterborough United were relegated from Nationwide Division Two	1997
387.	Jack Blood became manager of Peterborough United	1948
388.	David Gregory was transferred to Stoke City for £55,000	1977
389.	Goalkeeper David Seaman was called up for the England Under-21 squad	1984
390.	The Posh nickname for Peterborough United was started	1921

2002/2003

391.	Barnet
392.	Andy Clarke
393.	Luton Town
394.	Francis Green
395.	Mansfield Town
396.	11th
397.	Marc Joseph
398.	Simon Rea, Jimmy Bullard, Bradley Allen, David Farrell and Andy Clarke
399.	Leon McKenzie
400.	Barry Fry

YEARS AT THE CLUB – 1

401.	David Seaman	1982-84
402.	Jim Hall	1967-75
403.	Tommy Robson	1968-81
404.	Gary Breen	1994-96
405.	Marcus Ebdon	1991-97
406.	Leon McKenzie	2000-03
407.	Terry Bly	1960-62
408.	David Farrell	1997-2006
409.	Tony Philliskirk	1992-94
410.	Colin Clarke	1981-84

1980s

411.   Martin Wilkinson

412.   Robbie Cooke

413.   Mickey Gynn

414.   Colchester United and Hartlepool United

415.   False: they were beaten once

416.   18

417.   5th

418.   Ian Benjamin

419.   Mick Gooding

420.   Mick Jones

DIVISION THREE PLAY-OFF FINAL 1992

421.   Stockport County

422.   Ken Charlery

423.   Bobby Barnes

424.   Chris Turner

425.   25,000

426.   Steve Cooper

427.   Neil Edwards

428.   Fred Barber

429.   Stockport County 1-2 Peterborough United

430.   60,000

MATTHEW ETHERINGTON

431.   1981

432.   6

433.   Brentford

434.   Barry Fry

435.   Tottenham Hotspur

436.   3

437.   Leyton Orient

438.   51: 43 (8)

439.   Torquay United

440.   West Ham United

HOW MUCH DID THEY PAY? – 2

441.   Phil Crosby from Rotherham United, 1989   £42,500

442.	Fred Barber from Walsall, 1991	£25,000
443.	Ray Hankin from Middlesbrough, 1983	£5,000
444.	Tommy Robson from Newcastle United, 1968	£20,000
445.	Mick Lambert from Ipswich Town, 1979	£40,000
446.	Carl Griffiths from Portsmouth, 1996	£225,000
447.	Danny Carter from Leyton Orient, 1995	£25,000
448.	Paul Culpin from Northampton Town, 1989	£40,000
449.	David Robinson from Halifax Town, 1989	£100,000
450.	Harry Holman from Exeter City, 1978	£10,000

1970s

451.	John Barnwell
452.	Tommy Robson
453.	All 3 goals were penalties
454.	16th
455.	Manchester United
456.	Blackburn Rovers
457.	Bob Doyle, Ian Ross and Chris Turner
458.	26
459.	Mark Heeley
460.	Joe Cooke and Barry Butlin

YEARS AT THE CLUB – 2

461.	Jimmy Bullard	2001-03
462.	Tony Adcock	1992-94
463.	Derek Dougan	1963-65
464.	Andy Clarke	1999-2005
465.	David Pleat	1970-71
466.	Fred Barber	1991-94
467.	Paddy Sloan	1952-54
468.	Mickey Gynn	1979-83
469.	Mick Gooding	1987-88
470.	David Oldfield	2000-02

2001/2002

471.	Barry Fry
472.	Leon McKenzie
473.	Helgi Danielsson

474.	Bournemouth
475.	Queens Park Rangers
476.	17th
477.	Luke Steele
478.	0-0
479.	David Farrell, Francis Green and Leon McKenzie
480.	Leon McKenzie

POSITIONS THEY PLAYED – 1

481.	Fred Barber	Goalkeeper
482.	Billy McEwan	Midfield
483.	Joe Lewis	Goalkeeper
484.	Don Heath	Outside right
485.	Ellis Stafford	Fullback
486.	Bobby Barnes	Winger
487.	Sean St Ledger	Defender
488.	Mike Small	Striker
489.	Trevor Anderson	Forward
490.	Bert Murray	Winger

CHRIS TURNER

491.	Defender
492.	1951
493.	Luton Town
494.	Cambridge United
495.	37
496.	4
497.	Jim Iley, Noel Cantwell and John Barnwell
498.	1992 (December)
499.	Hereford United
500.	True

MATCH THE YEAR – 3

501.	Jack Fairbrother took over as manager of Peterborough Unit	1952
502.	Darragh MacAnthony joined Peterborough United as chairman	2006
503.	Jim Iley signs Richie Barker from Notts County	1971

504.	Bobby Barnes was born	1962
505.	The Posh only played 2 games during February due to the 'big freeze'	1947
506.	Percy Allen was born	1895
507.	Jimmy Bullard joined Wigan Athletic	2003
508.	David Pleat joined Peterborough United	1970
509.	Jimmy Quinn scored his 25th and last League goal for The Posh	1998
510.	Simon Davies joined Tottenham Hotspur for £700,000	2000

HAT-TRICKS

511.	v. Brentford (home), November 2007, League	Aaron McLean
512.	v. Hull City (away), November 1995, League	Gary Martindale
513.	v. Oxford United (home), September 1993, League	Tony Philliskirk
514.	v. Gillingham (away), November 1988, FA Cup 1st round	Dave Longhurst
515.	v. Newport County (away), April 1988, League	Steve Phillips
516.	v. Accrington Stanley (home), January 2008, League	Aaron McLean
517.	v. Portsmouth (home), January 1977, League	John Cozens
518.	v. Chester City (away), April 1978, League	Alan Slough
519.	v. Hartlepool United (home), February 1982, League	Robbie Cooke
520.	v. Staines (away), December 2007, FA Cup 2nd round	Craig Mackail-Smith

POSITIONS THEY PLAYED – 2

521.	David Farrell	Midfield
522.	Gordon Pulley	Winger
523.	Jim Walker	Fullback
524.	Mark Tyler	Goalkeeper

525.	Mark Peters	Defender
526.	Archie Styles	Left back
527.	George Berry	Centre back
528.	Paul Price	Central defender
529.	Aaron McLean	Striker
530.	Jon Sheffield	Goalkeeper

2000/2001

531. David Farrell
532. 12th
533. Leon McKenzie
534. Drewe Broughton
535. Cambridge United
536. Jason Lee and Simon Rae
537. Jason Lee
538. 59
539. Jason Lee
540. 15

DEREK DOUGAN

541. 1938
542. 43 (8 goals)
543. Aston Villa
544. The League Cup
545. 77
546. £4,000
547. Blackburn Rovers
548. 38
549. Leicester City
550. Kansas City Spurs

BIG WINS

551.	v. Brentford (home), November 2007, League	7-0
552.	v. Hartlepool United (home), October 2004, League	3-0
553.	v. Notts County (home), January 2004, League	5-2
554.	v. Rotherham (home), November 1996, League	6-2
555.	v. Torquay United (home), November 2006, League	5-2
556.	v. Oldham Athletic (away), August 2000, League	4-1

557.	v. Accrington Stanley (home), January 2008, League	8-2
558.	v. Wrexham (home), March 2004, League	6-1
559.	v. Bournemouth (home), September 2001, League	6-0
560.	v. Tranmere Rovers (home), March 2002, League	5-0

DAVID SEAMAN

561.	Rotherham
562.	MBE
563.	Queens Park Rangers
564.	Peterborough United
565.	£100,000
566.	Bobby Robson
567.	91
568.	Arsenal
569.	Leeds United
570.	75

LEAGUE GOALS DURING 2007/2008

571.	Chris Whelpdale	3
572.	Scott Rendell	3
573.	Danny Crow	2
574.	Dean Keates	5
575.	Rene Howe	1
576.	Aaron McLean	29
577.	George Boyd	12
578.	Charlie Lee	6
579.	Craig Mackail-Smith	12
580.	Craig Morgan	2

ADAM DRURY

581.	1978
582.	Peterborough United
583.	Norwich City
584.	Left back
585.	138 (10)
586.	2004
587.	2
588.	Barry Fry

589. **Gillingham**

590. **Watford**

JIMMY QUINN

591. **1997**

592. **Scunthorpe United**

593. **25**

594. **True**

595. **Barnet**

596. **Barry Fry**

597. **Southend United**

598. **Northern Ireland**

599. **Exeter City**

600. **5**

TONY ADCOCK

601. **1963**

602. **Striker**

603. **Colchester United (1981-87 and 1995-99)**

604. **David White and Paul Stewart**

605. **Northampton Town**

606. **107 (4)**

607. **£190,000**

608. **Northampton Town**

609. **35**

610. **Heybridge Swifts**

HIGHEST LEAGUE GOALSCORERS – 1

611.	1978/1979	Barry Butlin and Joe Cooke (5 goals)
612.	1979/1980	Billy Kellock (19 goals)
613.	1980/1981	Robbie Cooke (22 goals)
614.	1981/1982	Robbie Cooke (24 goals)
615.	1982/1983	Mickey Gynn (17 goals)
616.	1983/1984	Alan Waddle (12 goals)
617.	1984/1985	Errington Kelly (11 goals)
618.	1985/1986	Jackie Gallacher (12 goals)
619.	1986/1987	Steve Phillips (11 goals)
620.	1987/1988	Mick Gooding (18 goals)

DAVID FARRELL

621. Birmingham
622. Redditch United
623. £100,000
624. Aston Villa
625. 175 (21)
626. Midfield
627. Boston United
628. 26
629. Scunthorpe United
630. Burton Albion

AGAINST WHICH TEAM?

631. Darlington
632. Halifax Town
633. Gillingham
634. Barnet
635. Lincoln City
636. Aston Villa
637. Bournemouth
638. Carlisle United
639. Lincoln City
640. Huddersfield Town

MARK TYLER

641. Norwich
642. Goalkeeper
643. FIFA World Youth Championship
644. Yeovil Town
645. Peterborough United
646. Hull City
647. Birmingham City
648. Colchester United
649. Dan Connor
650. Ian Bennett

NOEL CANTWELL

651. Irish

652. **Fullback**

653. **1972**

654. **True**

655. **7th**

656. **Coventry City**

657. **1986**

658. **Cambridge United**

659. **Mick Jones**

660. **7th**

PLAYER OF THE YEAR

661.	**Ian Bennett**	**1993**
662.	**Tommy Robson**	**1974**
663.	**Adam Drury**	**1998**
664.	**Bob Doyle**	**1979**
665.	**Andy Clarke**	**2000**
666.	**Mick Gooding**	**1988**
667.	**Dave Longhurst**	**1989**
668.	**Dave Robinson**	**1990**
669.	**Billy Kellock**	**1980**
670.	**Ken Charlery**	**1995**

ANDY CLARKE

671. **Wimbledon**

672. **Mansfield Town**

673. **Brighton & Hove Albion**

674. **57**

675. **1999**

676. **True**

677. **15**

678. **Barry Fry**

679. **Torquay United**

680. **230: 170 (60)**

WORRELL STERLING

681. **Bethnal Green**

682. **Torquay United**

683. **Watford**

684. £70,000
685. 190 (3)
686. Rushden & Diamonds
687. All 46
688. Bristol Rovers
689. Midfield
690. 28

UNUSUAL RESULTS

691.	v. Hartlepool United (home), September 2006, League	3-5
692.	v. Peterborough (away), March 2005, League	0-5
693.	v. Exeter City (home), October 1989, League	4-3
694.	v. Bristol Rovers (home), September 2008, League	5-4
695.	v. Wycombe Wanderers (home), September 1996, League	6-3
696.	v. Chelsea (away), January 2001, FA Cup 3rd round	0-5
697.	v. Brighton & Hove Albion (away), November 1999, FA Cup 1st round replay	0-3
698.	v. Stoke City (home), February 2001, League	0-4
699.	v. Barnet (away), September 1998, League	9-1
700.	v. Hartlepool United (home), August 2003, League	3-4

POT LUCK

701. Mickey Gynn
702. Rotherham United
703. 17
704. 9
705. £8
706. 17
707. Errington Kelly

708.   Robbie Cooke

709.   47

710.   Alan Slough (30th, 61st and 89th minutes)

FOURTH DIVISION CHAMPIONSHIP – 1973/1974

711.   Noel Cantwell

712.   27

713.   Tommy Robson

714.   19

715.   John Cozens

716.   Mansfield Town

717.   Jim Hall

718.   2nd

719.   True

720.   Jim Hall, John Cozens and Mick Jones

APPEARANCES FOR THE CLUB

721.	Mick Halsall	316 (1)
722.	Tommy Robson	514 (45)
723.	Noel Luke	336 (10)
724.	Chris Turner	357 (7)
725.	Jack Carmichael	394 (26)
726.	Worrell Sterling	234 (3)
727.	Peter McNamee	212
728.	Jim Hall	329 (5)
729.	David Farrell	207 (23)
730.	John Crawford	196

AARON McLEAN

731.   Grays Athletic

732.   £150,000

733.   True

734.   Leyton Orient

735.   Leyton Orient

736.   Striker

737.   2

738.   Brentford (League, November 2007) and Accrington Stanley (League, January 2008)

739.   Grimsby Town

740.   2006

TOMMY ROBSON

741.   Gateshead

742.   1968

743.   Newcastle United

744.   John Cozens and Freddie Hill

745.   14

746.   111

747.   Northampton Town

748.   440 (42)

749.   Watford (5th, 76th and 88th minutes)

750.   1978

HIGHEST LEAGUE GOALSCORERS – 2

751.	1988/1989	Nick Cusack (10 goals)
752.	1989/1990	Mick Halsall (11 goals)
753.	1990/1991	Paul Culpin (10 goals)
754.	1991/1992	Ken Charlery (16 goals)
755.	1992/1993	Tony Adcock (16 goals)
756.	1993/1994	Tony Adcock (12 goals)
757.	1994/1995	Ken Charlery (16 goals)
758.	1995/1996	Gary Martindale (15 goals)
759.	1996/1997	Scott Houghton (8 goals)
760.	1997/1998	Jimmy Quinn (20 goals)

CLUB GOALSCORERS

761.	Worrell Sterling	38
762.	Jim Hall	137
763.	Andy Clarke	27
764.	Chris Turner	43
765.	Tommy Robson	128
766.	Terry Bly	87
767.	Peter McNamee	68
768.	Leon McKenzie	42
769.	Ken Charlery	80
770.	Tony Adcock	39

GEORGE BOYD

771. 2007
772. Midfielder
773. Stevenage Borough
774. Darlington
775. True
776. 6
777. Accrington Stanley
778. 12
779. 1985
780. Football League Trophy

TERRY BLY

781. 1935
782. Striker
783. Norwich City
784. 52
785. 88
786. Coventry City
787. Grantham Town
788. 81
789. 1970
790. 719

HIGHEST LEAGUE GOALSCORERS – 3

791.	1998/1999	Giuliano Grazioli (15 goals)
792.	1999/2000	Andy Clarke (15 goals)
793.	2000/2001	Leon McKenzie (13 goals)
794.	2001/2002	Leon McKenzie (18 goals)
795.	2002/2003	Andy Clarke (16 goals)
796.	2003/2004	Leon McKenzie (10 goals)
797.	2004/2005	Callum Willock (12 goals)
798.	2005/2006	Danny Crow (15 goals)
799.	2006/2007	Craig Mackail-Smith (8 goals)
800.	2007/2008	Aaron McLean (29 goals)

NOTES

NOTES

NOTES

NOTES

NOTES

NOTES

NOTES

NOTES

www.apexpublishing.co.uk